JuSTiN's RHyme Time

JuSTiN FLeTCHeR

Illustrated by Patrick Tate

faber and faber

First published in 2013
by Faber and Faber Limited
Bloomsbury House
74-77 Great Russell Street
London WC1B 3DA

Designed by Patrick Tate
Printed in England by CPI Group (UK) Ltd, Croydon CR0 4YY

The right of Justin Fletcher to be identified as author of this
work has been asserted in accordance with Section 77 of
the Copyright, Designs and Patents Act 1988

A CIP record for this book is available from the British
Library

Hello, girls and boys!

I'm off to spend the day in Nursery Rhyme Land. Would you like to come with me?
We might meet some people you know - and learn some great new rhymes, too.

Come on, let's go!
Love,

JuSTiN

X

Hello, Little Miss Muffet! What's that you're eating? It looks very tasty.

Hello, Justin! Would you like some curds and whey?

3

Little Miss Muffet

Little Miss Muffet
Sat on a tuffet
Eating her curds and whey.

Along came a spider
Who sat down beside her
And frightened
    Miss Muffet away!

I think spiders are very clever. They can spin such beautiful webs.

7

And they're very good at climbing.

8

Incey-Wincey Spider

Incey-Wincey Spider
Climbed up the water spout.
Down came the rain
And washed the spider out.

Out came the sun
And dried up all the rain.
And the Incey-Wincey Spider
Climbed up the spout again.

Hello, Mary!

Hi Justin! Look at my flowers.

13

Mary, Mary,
Quite Contrary

Mary, Mary,
Quite contrary.
How does your garden
 grow?

With silver bells
And cockle shells
And pretty maids
All in a row.

Come and smell these lovely roses ...Ah - ah - atishoo!

17

Oh dear - those roses
are making me sneeze!

A-A-A-TISHOOOOOOOO!!!

Ring-a Ring-a Rosies

Ring-a ring-a rosies
A pocket full of posies
A-tishoo!
A-tishoo!
We all fall down.

I Had A Little
Nut Tree

I had a little nut tree
Nothing would it bear
But a silver nutmeg
And a golden pear.

The King of Spain's daughter
Came to visit me
And all for the sake
Of my little nut tree.

24

And I can see someone else playing in the garden - a little teddy bear. Hello, teddy!

Round and Round the Garden

Round and round the garden
Like a teddy bear,
One step,
Two steps,
Tickle you under there!

29

Here We Go Round the Mulberry Bush

Here we go round the
Mulberry bush,
The mulberry bush,
The mulberry bush.
Here we go round
The mulberry bush,
So early in the morning.

32

33

34

Doctor Foster

Doctor Foster
Went to Gloucester
In a shower of rain.
He fell in a puddle
Right up to his middle
And never went there again.

37

It's Raining, It's Pouring

It's raining, it's pouring
The old man is snoring.
He went to bed,
And bumped his head
And couldn't get up
In the morning!

40

The sound of marching feet - walking down the street . . .

The Grand Old Duke of York

Oh, the grand old Duke of York,
He had ten thousand men,
He marched them up
To the top of the hill,
And he marched them
Down again.

And when they were up,
They were up.
And when they were down,
They were down.
And when they were only
Half-way up,
They were neither
Up nor down.

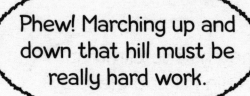

44

Jack and Jill

Jack and Jill
Went up the hill
To fetch a pail of water
Jack fell down
And broke his crown
And Jill came tumbling after.

Up Jack got,
And home did trot
As fast as he could caper
He went to bed
And bound his head
With vinegar and brown paper.

Now there's someone else who's always having accidents. Do you know who? It's good old Humpty Dumpty, of course!

Humpty Dumpty

Humpty Dumpty
Sat on a wall
Humpty Dumpty
Had a great fall.
All the King's horses
And all the King's men
Couldn't put Humpty
Together again.

51

Look, here's the Royal Palace, straight ahead. I wonder if the King and Queen are at home?

Sing a Song
of Sixpence

Sing a song of sixpence,
    a pocket full of rye,
Four and twenty blackbirds,
    baked in a pie.
When the pie was opened,
    the birds began to sing.
Wasn't that a dainty dish
    to set before a King?

The King was in his
  counting house
Counting out his money.
The Queen was in
  the parlour
Eating bread and honey.

The maid was in the garden
  Hanging out the clothes.
When down came a blackbird
  And pecked off her nose!

If I were King for a day, I'd wear an enormous crown and have a big party. Would *you* like to be King or Queen for a day?

58

Lavender's Blue

Lavender's blue, dilly, dilly
Lavender's green.
When I am King, dilly, dilly
You shall be Queen.

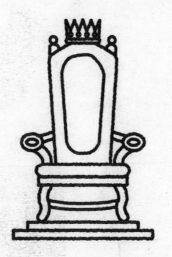

Pussy Cat, Pussy Cat

Pussy cat, pussy cat
Where have you been?
I've been to London
To visit the Queen.

Pussy cat, pussy cat
What did you there?
I frightened a little mouse
Under the chair.

That poor little mouse. Oh, hang on. Look!

Hickory Dickory Dock

Hickory dickory dock,
The mouse ran up the clock.
The clock struck one,
The mouse ran down,
Hickory dickory dock!

I know three more
mice that can run
really fast. Here they
come right now!

Three Blind Mice

Three blind mice,
    three blind mice.
See how they run,
    see how they run.

They all ran after
    the farmer's wife
Who cut off their tails
    with a carving knife.
You've never seen
    such a thing in your life
As three blind mice!

But I have got some more furry friends for you to meet. Three lovely little kittens . . .

The Three
Little Kittens

The three little kittens,
They lost their mittens,
And they began to cry.
'Oh Mother dear,
See here, see here,
Our mittens we have lost.'

'You've lost your mittens?
You naughty kittens!
Then you shall have no pie.'

'Meow, meow, meow, meow!'
'We shall have no pie!'

Now look who's here - it's a boy called Jack and he **loves** pie! Yum . . .

Little Jack Horner

Little Jack Horner
Sat in the corner
Eating a Christmas pie.

He put in his thumb
And pulled out a plum
And said 'What a good
    boy am I!'

Georgie Porgie

Georgie Porgie,
Pudding and pie,
Kissed the girls
And made them cry.

When the boys
Came out to play
Georgie Porgie ran away.

Pease Pudding Hot

Pease pudding hot
Pease pudding cold
Pease pudding in a pot
Nine days old.

Some like it hot
Some like it cold
Some like it in a pot
Nine days old.

Hot Cross Buns

Hot cross buns!
Hot cross buns!
One a penny, two a penny,
Hot cross buns!

If you have no daughters
Give them to your sons.
One a penny, two a penny,
Hot cross buns!

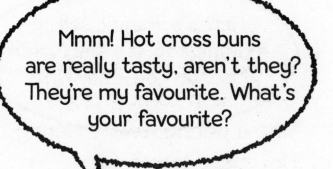

Do You Know the Muffin Man?

Do you know the Muffin Man,
The Muffin Man,
The Muffin Man?
Do you know the Muffin Man
Who lives on Drury Lane?

Yes, I know the Muffin Man,
The Muffin Man,
The Muffin Man.
Yes, I know the Muffin Man
Who lives on Drury Lane.

Polly Put the Kettle On

Polly put the kettle on,
Polly put the kettle on.
Polly put the kettle on,
We'll all have tea.

Suki take it off again.
Suki take it off again.
Suki take it off again,
They've all gone away.

I'm A Little Teapot

I'm a little teapot
Short and stout!
Here's my handle
Here's my spout.

When I get all steamed up
Hear me shout!
Tip me up
And pour me out.

98

Little Bo Peep

Little Bo Peep
Has lost her sheep
And doesn't know
Where to find them.

Leave them alone
And they'll come home
Wagging their tails
Behind them.

Baa Baa Black Sheep

Baa, baa, black sheep,
Have you any wool?
Yes, sir, yes, sir,
Three bags full.

One for the master,
And one for the dame,
And one for the little boy
Who lives down the lane.

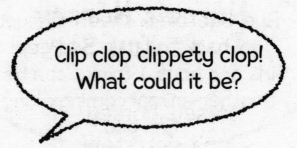

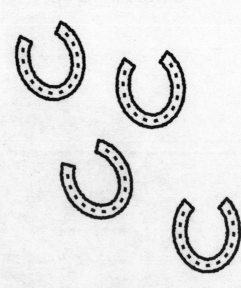

Horsey, Horsey, Don't You Stop

Horsey, horsey,
Don't you stop!
Just let your feet go
Clippety clop.

Your tail goes swish,
And the wheels go round.
Giddy-up!
We're homeward bound.

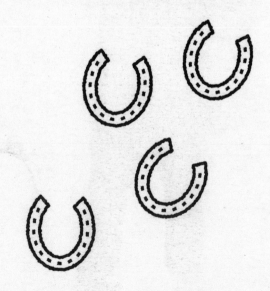

109

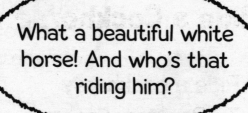

What a beautiful white horse! And who's that riding him?

Ride a Cockhorse

Ride a cockhorse
To Banbury Cross,
To see a fine lady
Upon a white horse.

Rings on her fingers,
And bells on her toes,
She shall have music,
Wherever she goes.

113

This Little Piggy

This little piggy went to
   market
This little piggy stayed at
   home
This little piggy had roast
   beef
This little piggy had none.

And this little piggy went . . .
'Wee wee wee' all the way
home!

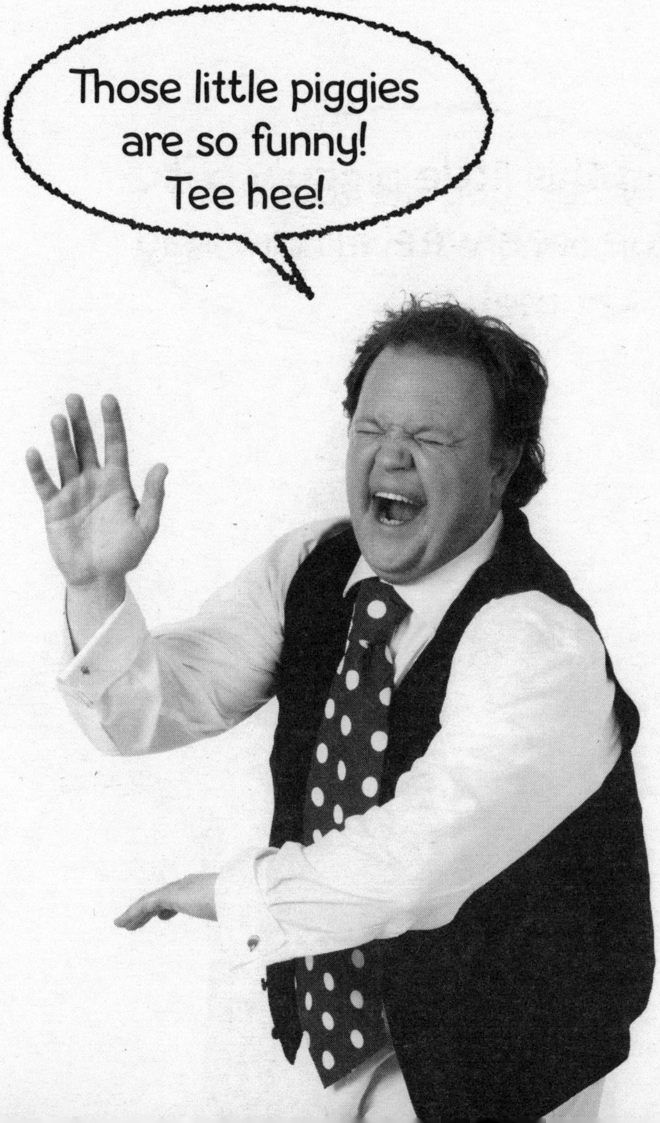
Those little piggies are so funny! Tee hee!

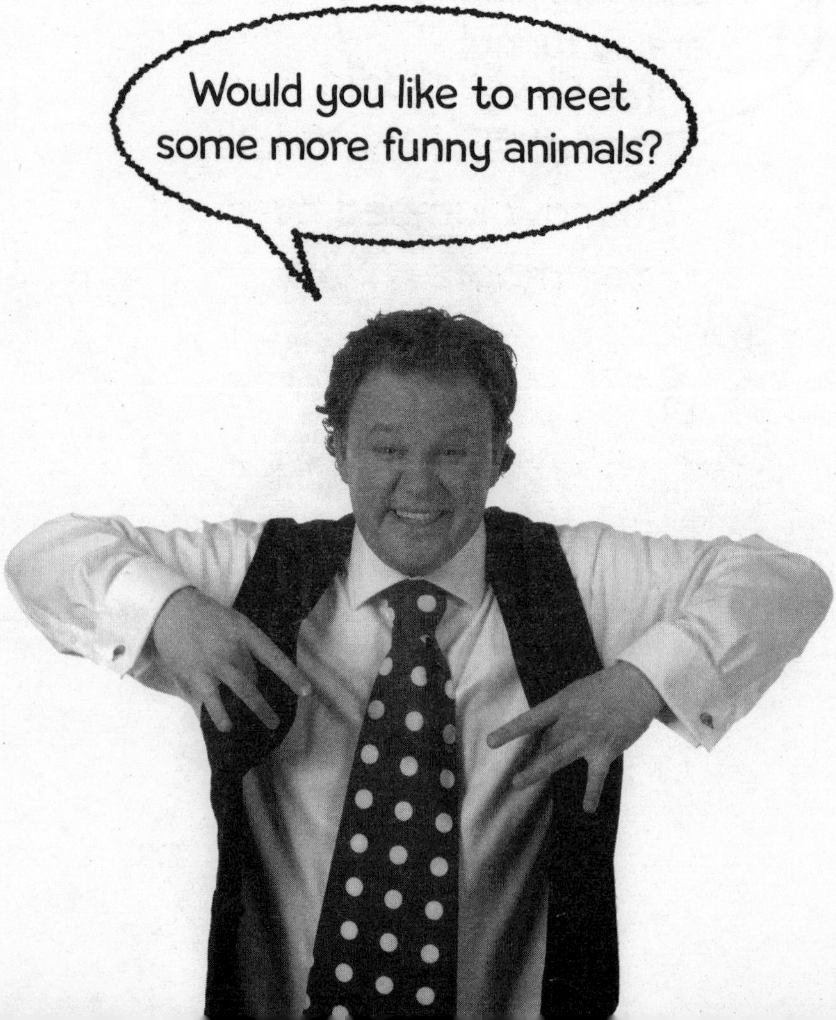
Would you like to meet some more funny animals?

Hey Diddle Diddle

Hey, diddle diddle,
The cat and the fiddle,
The cow jumped over
 the moon.

The little dog laughed
To see such fun
And the dish ran away with
   the spoon.

Oh dear - my shoe is broken! Better find someone who can mend it.

Cobbler, Cobbler, Mend My Shoe

Cobbler, cobbler,
    mend my shoe,
Get it done
    by half-past two.
Do it neat,
    and do it strong,
And I will pay you
    when it's done.

Thanks very much, Mr Cobbler!

What a helpful cobbler!

See-Saw, Marjorie Daw

See-saw, Majorie Daw,
Johnny shall have
A new master.
He shall have
But a penny a day,
Because he won't
Work any faster.

Jack Be Nimble

Jack, be nimble
Jack, be quick
Jack, jump over
The candlestick.

Jack jumped high
Jack jumped low
Jack jumped over
And burned his toe.

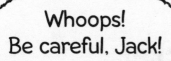

131

Lucy Locket
Lost Her Pocket

Lucy Locket
Lost her pocket
Kitty Fisher found it.

Not a penny
Was there in it
Only ribbon round it.

Oh look, here's a little stream. Wouldn't it be nice to get a boat and go for a row?

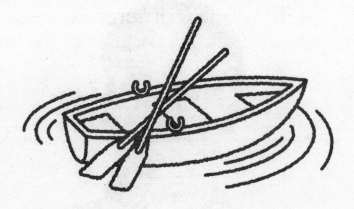

Row, Row, Row
Your Boat

Row, row, row your boat,
Gently down the stream.
Merrily, merrily,
Merrily, merrily,
Life is but a dream.

Row, row, row your boat,
Gently down the stream.
If you see a crocodile,
Don't forget to scream.
Aaah!

I was enjoying that boat ride before that silly crocodile came along!!

Wee Willie Winkie

Wee Willie Winkie
Runs through the town.
Upstairs, downstairs,
In his night gown.
Tapping at the window
Crying through
   the locks
Are the children
   all asleep?
It's past eight o'clock.

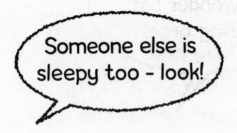

Someone else is sleepy too - look!

141

Little Boy Blue

Little Boy Blue
Come blow your horn
The sheep are in the
    meadow
The cows are in the corn.

But where is the boy
Who looks after the sheep?
He's under the hay stack
Fast asleep.

Will you wake him?
No, not I.
For if I do
He's sure to cry.

144

Look, someone else is sleeping too. A little baby.

Rock-a-Bye Baby

Rock-a-bye baby, on the
   tree top.
When the wind blows,
   the cradle will rock.
When the bough breaks,
   the cradle will fall
And down will come baby,
   cradle and all.

Wow, what a busy day we've had in Nursery Rhyme Land!

Goodbye, boys and girls.

I've loved sharing these nursery rhymes with you. I hope you enjoyed our trip!

Love,

JUSTIN FLETCHER

Justin Fletcher has worked as an actor, children's television presenter and voice-over artist for the past fifteen years. In 2008 he won a BAFTA for best children's television presenter and was awarded an MBE for his services to children's television and the charity sector.

In BAFTA's 2010 Children's Awards, Justin's series

Something Special won the Pre-School Live Action award, and he won his second award for best presenter. Justin's voice-over work includes the BAFTA-winning programme *The Tweenies*. He is also the 'voice' of Shaun in *Shaun the Sheep*.

Justin has written a number of children's books including *Justin's Chuckle Time*.

Hello, everyone!
Are you ready to giggle?

How do you start an insect race?

One, two, flea, go!

What kind of dog likes bubble baths?

A shampoodle.

Watch out - these jokes will make you laugh out loud!

Love,
JuSTin X